Scholastic Phonics

Gran's Kite

Published in the UK by Scholastic Education, 2022
Scholastic Distribution Centre, Bosworth Avenue, Tournament Fields, Warwick, CV34 6UQ
Scholastic Ireland, 89E Lagan Road, Dublin Industrial Estate, Glasnevin, Dublin, D11 HP5F

SCHOLASTIC and associated logos are trademarks and/or registered trademarks of Scholastic Inc.
www.scholastic.co.uk
© 2022 Scholastic
1 2 3 4 5 6 7 8 9   2 3 4 5 6 7 8 9 0 1

Printed by Ashford Colour Press
The book is made of materials from well-managed, FSC®-certified forests and other controlled sources.

A CIP catalogue record for this book is available from the British Library.

ISBN 978-0702-30915-1

All rights reserved. This book is sold subject to the condition that it shall not, by way of trade or otherwise, be lent, hired out or otherwise circulated in any form of binding or cover other than that in which it is published. No part of this publication may be reproduced, stored in a retrieval system, or transmitted in any form or by any other means (electronic, mechanical, photocopying, recording or otherwise) without prior written permission of Scholastic Limited.

Every effort has been made to trace copyright holders for the works reproduced in this publication, and the publishers apologise for any inadvertent omissions.

Author
Ann Hill
Editorial team
Rachel Morgan, Vicki Yates, Fiona Undrill, Jennie Clifford
Design team
Dipa Mistry, Justin Hoffmann, Andrea Lewis, We Are Grace
Illustrations
Alejandra Barajas/Advocate Art

Help your child to read!

This book practises these letters and letter sounds.
Point and say the sounds with your child:

- o (as in 'go')
- i (as 'behind')
- e (as in 'be')
- i-e (as in 'kite')
- o-e (as in 'hope')
- ew (as in 'flew')
- ie (as in 'field')

Your child may need help to read these common tricky words:

- to
- the
- said
- they
- you
- have
- my
- there
- was
- of
- sure
- would

Before reading
- Look at the cover picture and read the title together. Read the back cover blurb to your child.
- Ask your child: *Have you seen a kite? What was it like?*

During reading
- If your child gets stuck on a word, remind them to sound it out and then blend the sounds to read the word: b-l-ew, blew.
- If they are still stuck, show them how to read the word.
- Enjoy looking at the pictures together. Pause to talk about the story.

After reading
- Ask your child: *At the end, did Leo like the bright kites best? Why not?*
- *What would you like to play with on a field?*

"Let's go shopping," said Gran. "We need eggs and cookies."

Leo gazed up.
A bright kite flew high, close to the clouds.

"They cost too much," said Gran. "But you can have my kite!"

Going home, they saw five bright new kites.

There was no hope of winning with Gran's old kite.

At home, Gran said, "I'll find my kite. It's a fine kite, Leo!"

Leo was sure Gran's kite would be useless.

Gran appeared from the shed holding a ragged old thing.

"This will win, Leo!" she said, shaking off the dust.

The next day, they took the kite to the field.
Bright kites flew in the sunshine.

"Let's just go home, Gran," said Leo.

Gran tugged the strings.
The kite opened and flew.

"It's like a bird!" shrieked Leo.

"Take the strings," said Gran.
Leo used the strings to make the kite-bird dive.

It dived down, then up,
up to the clouds.
Gran beamed like a child.

The bright kites bobbed behind the dark, rising bird.

The man smiled at Leo.
"You win the prize!" he said.
Gran and Leo did a high five.
"Gran's kite is the best!" Leo cried.

Retell the story